ASYA PEKUROVSKAYA

Second Book of the First Series

Spark, the Stone Man

Illustrated by Olga Titova

Pekasus
Factory of Animated Dreams

Don't open new worlds, open your eyes!

Published by Pekasus, 2011

Written by Asya Pekurovskaya
Illustrated by Olga Titova
Consulting Movie Director Aida Zyablikova
Edited by Tim Grundmann
Layout by Valentine Pavlovsky

ISBN: 978-0-9828487-3-9
Library of Congress Control Number 2010911130

Spark The Stone Man.
Second Book of the First Series

First Book Summary.

The icy range of the Granite Mountains looks desolate. Yet living in it are the stonemasons whose life is flinty as the granite they hew, and their laws are merciless.

At the foot of Granite Mountain lies the verdant, luxuriant Lemon Drop Valley. But no one can descend there, for the only access to the Valley is kept secret by the Royal House of stonemasons. Nevertheless, our little hero, whose name appears on the title, learns the secret and finds his way to the Valley.

There he is captivated by lingering, intoxicating smells of tropical plants, is greeted by twin moons, encounters a giant who converses with a monument, finds himself strolling on a splendid seaside promenade, falls in love with a local beauty, and teams up (under very strange circumstances) with a confectioner who helps him sneak into the Great wizard's castle. Once inside the castle, he witnesses a secret Forum of wizards in action, as well as frightening transformations performed by the magic Mash-fatum.

Just when he feels at ease in the magical Valley, Spark latches onto the illusory nature of his expectations and with a broken heart, he resolves to return home.

Many thanks to Serge Shats for inauguration.

Boundless gratitude to Aida Zyablikova for her relentless participation, for criticism and encouragement. Without her this book would have never been written.

To Stella

«Medun's Fibs»

When he stepped on a mountain rock that marked the beginning of the "Coveted Path," Spark was about to give himself up to soaring. However, the joy he had felt when he descended to the Valley was no longer there.

As much as Spark tried to dismiss thoughts of Lemon Drop Valley from his mind, they fluttered back in the form of little leaflets proclaiming that the Valley was ILLUSORY! ... CHIMERICAL! ... and FLASHY!

It wasn't clear where these leaflets came from, but the more Spark realized how ILLUSORY!, CHIMERICAL! and FLASHY! the Valley proved to be, the more intently he repeated to himself: "There are more things to delight in than Lemon Drop Valley! And Tonino was right when he said that I 'descended from the heights as cat's pajamas'!"

Yet when he reached the stone ledge where he liked to chisel his toys, he felt warm, salty droplets falling down his face.

"But was he right, indeed? Why did Tonino decide that 'cat's pajamas' was me?"

A black cat with a yellow bow tie came to Spark's mind. It looked exactly like the one he had eavesdropped on in Bertha the Mouse's dream! Mentally he started to dress it in pajamas. The cat didn't like it one bit and scratched and hissed, but Spark stood his ground and finally got the job done. Yet, as it turned out, he had put two buttons into one buttonhole, and two of the cat's back paws in a pajama leg. Spark wanted to set things straight, but the cat flew out of his arms — actually flew with a strange limp. Spark never would have believed that one could limp and fly at the same time, but he saw it with his own eyes! Moreover, the limping cat was flying so fast that Spark couldn't catch up with it even in his thoughts.

"But again, why did Tonino decide that 'cat's pajamas' was me?" Spark went on grilling himself when he noticed an effigy in his hands...

"I made a sculpture and didn't even notice how I did it! And it resembles Stella the Yushka as two drops of water!" Spark marveled pleased that he could carry through his old ambition...

But could he?

In his reverie he had seen Stella as a fairy tale princess with white hair buried deep into the ground.

And should one tell him now that the effigy in his hands had little in common with Stella the Yushka and resembled the princess even less, he wouldn't have believed it!

Reveling in his creation, he recalled the pledge that he gave to Tonino never to come back to the Valley.

"How wonderful it would have been, had I never said those words and Tonino never heard them!"

Then his thoughts took another turn as his fingers touched Tonino's gift in his pocket.

It was a miniature book with a sparkling glass mechanism depicted on its cover. He opened the book and read: "Get Your Spoonful of Boon — with the Fibs from Medun." And on the lower right corner there was a signature of the author: "Medun the Senior."

Spark turned the page.

"Do you know to whom Lemon Drop Valley should be thankful for its luminous glory? Oh, it was a race of Inventors, who dashed through the Valley like a comet, leaving a magnificent mark after it. 'Every man has a fool in his sleeve,' people said of them in the land of their birth, locking their doors before them. For what the Inventors grasped as clear and simple, others had perceived as wild fantasies. That's why the Inventors couldn't find a place to live, wandering from one land to the other, until Lemon Drop Valley graciously accepted them."

"Who were these Inventors after all?" Spark wondered aloud.

"Oh, they were the characters with heads swarming with schemes, plans and projects," the author informed him, quenching Spark's curiosity. "One of the Inventors, a true genius, had built the magical Mash-fatum, the wondrous machine capable of fulfilling all wishes.

"Another Inventor didn't have as much luck. Rumor had it that he didn't even finish his project before he died, letting no one know of its purpose. Basically, it was a mechanism thrust in a glass cube and installed right on the candied lemon sand. Perhaps, because his first encounter with this contraption ended up by his giving the glass cube a sound whack with his head, which made a resounding noise that sounded like '*Kaboom!*' — its proud new owner, Narcissus the Murmose, gave it a whimsical name, 'Aboo-Kaboom' (although he conceded that one could call it simply '*Kaboom*').

"And here is what was really amazing. The 'Aboo-Kaboom,' the purpose of which no one understood, was praised as if it were superior to the Mash-fatum! And that was wildly unreasonable!"

Yet as soon as Spark realized the absurdity of the comparison, a blinding smokescreen fell before his eyes and the book shut by itself. Immediately he was filled with an overpowering urge to rollick straight back to Lemon Drop Valley in a headlong dash!

This urge, alas, was stopped in its tracks. No sooner had he made his first step on the soft and warm sand, having inhaled the perfumed scent of Lemon Drop Valley (and before even noticing that the smokescreen had disappeared), someone grabbed him from the back and started spinning him until a familiar cook's cap flew into the air.

"Tonino!" Spark shouted. "What are you doing here?"

"Waiting for you," Tonino replied.

Tale II

Proposal

Walking along the promenade next to Tonino, Spark couldn't wait to see the real glass mechanism. If it looked anything as glittering and tantalizing as the picture on the miniature book cover...

"Here it is, 'Aboo-Kaboom'!" Tonino proclaimed, as if he read his thoughts. He was pointing towards the seashore, where a huge boulder lay resting on the sand.

The fog made it hard to tell what exactly it was. It seemed to resemble a walrus... or a seal... or maybe, Spark thought, a walrus and a seal combined in one being.

"But where is the machine?" he asked and stopped short.

A strange creature, dark and goblin-sized, developed from the fog like a negative film image. As it sharpened into focus, Spark could see he wore a leather backpack and, most improbably, a red jockey hat! The creature hopped onto the boulder and then smartly whipped its cover off with a masterful flick of his wrist.

The cover turned out to be a parachute cupola. But what it revealed before Spark's astonished eyes was a glass mechanism that was, truth to tell, not glittering and tantalizing as the miniature book cover had depicted it, but glowing with a gentle lilac moonlight that lit its elaborate vaulted ceiling.

A labyrinth of various glass trails appeared before Spark's eyes. Some trailed upwards while others raced downwards, passing and sometimes crossing each other to form channels of different shapes and lengths. Two glass baskets attached to transparent hoses were hanging from the central channel.

At that moment, the goblin (who now looked more like a dwarf, Spark thought) jumped inside the machine and dangled, holding on to the glass basket.

"What's he doing?" Spark wondered.

The goblin looking more like a dwarf jumped down, took out a collapsible plane table, a pen, a measuring tape, and a compass from his leather backpack, and began making a detailed sketch of "Aboo-Kaboom" on paper. Spark was delighted.

10

"So this is what a true Inventor is!" he whispered.

And the more pencil sketches appeared on the goblin's plane table, the greater admiration Spark felt for him.

"Just what dirty trick is this draftsman cooking?" Tonino thought in turn, also keeping his eye locked on the dwarf.

As you see, Tonino and Spark had two incompatible story lines in their heads and, as each reflected on his own thoughts, neither suspected how far he was from the other.

But what happened next literally exploded their silent discord.

From out of nowhere a cabriolet came crashing past them, accompanied by an ear-piercing holler: "Off with you, picaroon, or I'll fire!"

The cabriolet came to a sudden stop, raising a cloud of sand, and off jumped the overheated driver, his rifle aimed and ready.

The dwarf wasn't perturbed a bit.

"Dear me! You must be the one, the one I am — !" he said with the sweetest voice and bowed down before Narcissus the Murmose, as if too dazzled to finish his sentence. "And I lament," he continued, throwing a burning glance towards Aboo-Kaboom, "that I never suspected that you own that precious treasure..."

As he zealously turned his head towards Aboo-Kaboom he bumped into the glass wall, producing the signature *kaboom*! sound that gave the contraption its name.

"Intriguing design, don't you think?" he continued, flashing his ruby-red eyes. "Yet I can lay open its true purpose to you... or, as some say, its terrible secret... But you don't even know who you are talking to! Let me introduce myself! I am Zhabrey the Engineer!"

"Why would I care if you were an engineer," Narcissus interrupted him belligerently, "when you are first and foremost a rogue!"

"Oh, it matters a good deal!" the dwarf replied in a sonorous voice. "We speak here of a Major Engineering Project. And, in all humility I must confess that your humble servant can tinker and tune this glass creation to produce miraculous transformations!"

Narcissus produced a short guttoral sound, his attention instantly roused.

And it's understandable. Who in his right mind would insist on clinging to good manners before having grasped what this ruby-eyed Liliputian in a red jockey cap meant by "miraculous transformations"?

"Could you clarify your thought with a vivid example, perhaps?" Narcissus mumbled.

"Dead right I could," the dwarf consented, "and with a vivid one indeed. Follow my thought now... A dressed-up crowd of idlers observes a beauty under your trust, or, rather, a simple Yushka, to turn into a heavenly, chocolate-colored chinchilla! How about that?!"

Captivated, Narcissus was already seizing every word.

"You deliver the beauty, I do the miracle!"

At the word "miracle," the dwarf produced a pointer, touched the first basket with it, and suddenly little balloons of various colors started to roll, exploding geysers of paint in all directions.

"Impressed? I thought so," summarized the Engineer, moving his face directly against the cube's wall... and, as Narcissus imagined, having shown a devilish face to him (let's not forget that the interlocutors were placed on opposite sides of a glass barrier). "Why not make tomorrow an opening day? That is, if the night won't be too long for you to wait!"

While Narcissus was shaken to his core, his mind playing out the prospects sweeping before him, the dwarf readied to make his next move. But first he made a few steps away from Narcissus as a precaution.

"Sir, I can see you appreciate the grandeur of my project! At this time, may I suggest that we briefly touch on the delicate matter of my fees?"

Narcissus immediately regained his senses, throwing a hostile glance at his interlocutor. "Fees! Just who, pray tell, is paying whom!"

"Now, now," the dwarf responded instantly, "it just occurred to me that remuneration is customarily considered the crowning moment of every endeavor. However, if this idea appears novel to you, I suppose the matter of fees could be dropped."

Both players in the drama now frankly stared at one another.

Narcissus contemplated the transformational powers of Aboo-Kaboom as promised him by the dwarf. In his imagination he pictured a magnificent, foamy wave breaking ashore, leaving thousands of chinchillas in its wake.

"From now on," he thought in triumph, "chinchillas will be guarding my Aboo-Kaboom!"

The dwarf triumphed as well. After all, hadn't he just managed to save himself from being blown sky-high? And best of all, the dwarf's complete drawing of the Aboo-Kaboom was safely tucked away in his backpack!

Zhabrey the Engineer

What a scam artist!" said Tonino, following the disappearing dwarf with eyes narrowed with suspicion. "Spun a yarn a mile long and faded away!"

"Why a scam artist?" Spark responded.

"Don't you see why?"

"What am I to see? Isn't he an engineer?"

"You mean Zhabrey? An engineer? All he does is make crafty designs! On occasions, the Inventors could teach him a thing or two about transformations!"

"Is he something of a wizard then?"

"Other dwarves might have thought so once, when he tried to talk them into building an underground labyrinth connecting Lemon Drop Valley with the rest of the world."

"Whoa, one can perhaps travel from Lemon Drop Valley?" Spark asked and his heart started to race.

"One could, if it were not for Zhabrey..."

Tonino noted Spark's interest, yet he didn't rush to narrate. When telling a tale, he liked to keep his audience in agonizing suspense.

"See," he continued at last, "the dwarves were natural-born jewelers, masters of precious ornaments highly valued in the Valley of Foggy Albion. There they carried their jeweled creations to sell, until Zhabrey sabotaged their paths."

"And how did he manage to do it?" fired Spark eagerly.

"Zhabrey simply looked for the dwarves lucky enough to find the most valuable stones, and then lured them into traps... The dwarves tolerated that for a while, and finally kicked him out of the underground kingdom."

Tonino paused for breath. Now it was he, not Spark, who waited for a reaction. But Spark was silent.

"Now Zhabrey lives in a dungeon," Tonino went on. "The entrance into his dwelling is built in such a tricky way that when you're standing right in front of it, you think that you're facing a sheer cliff. And yet the impression of a cliff is nothing but an illusion: one simply mistakes a stair leading up for the vertical ledge. What did I tell you? Crafty!"

"But if he is such a villain," Spark started cautiously, "can we let him turn the beautiful Yushka into some chinchilla?"

"I thought of that, too. There must be a trap there!"

Spark suddenly rushed about in a panic.

"Then why are we standing here? We must warn the Yushkas of the trap!"

Clozed for the Nite

No matter how quickly Tonino walked, he couldn't catch up with Spark, who ran ahead in order to privately practice the speech he planned to deliver when he met Stella.

"First I'll explain to her what a real and all the more super-real danger threatens her. And when she asks for help, I will tell her that this real or super-real danger might be averted — with my help!"

Yet Spark was then struck by the realization that he had no inkling as to how to deal with any danger, no matter how real, super-real, or unreal it might be.

Should something like this happen on Granite Mountain, he would simply gather the stonemasons and get the King involved. But how are these things handled here in Lemon Drop Valley? And who knows how to protect a helpless Yushka from the devilish cunning of Zhabrey the Dwarf?

"Hmm... Perhaps I should find Narcissus the Murmose," Spark mused. "As soon as he learns that Zhabrey is not the great inventor he pretends to be but a fib-fabricator, he will simply call off the opening of the Aboo-Kaboom. And then... things will turn out splendidly well... Only one needs to hurry up!"

As Spark's thoughts continued in this up-and-down fashion, from optimistic heights to the depths of despair, the landscape kept changing as well. The promenade was now far behind them as they made their way through a dense and dark forest.

"Can't we take a short-cut? I can't see a thing!" said Spark, breaking the low-hanging branch that hit his head.

"This is a short-cut!" came Tonino's reply from a tiny distance away. "If we were not in such a rush, we could have gone around this fo — "

At that moment something collapsed and clicked. Then it cracked many times, shifted and quieted down. And Tonino's holler reached Spark's ears.

"What happened?" Spark shouted in alarm.

"I'm in a trap!"

"You're in a trap?!" That was all Spark could utter as he struggled to trace the source of the voice. If he sounded a little too fearful, that was because he hadn't seen a single trap in his life!

"Keep talking or else I'll never find you," Spark called out.

"Watch out!" Tonino declared. "I hope you do not, if possible, walk into another trap!"

But Spark was already safely at his side. He grabbed Tonino's hand and started pulling him up.

"Ouch! It hurts!" Tonino screamed. "Lift the trigger first!"

When Spark managed to unclench the teeth of the trap and free Tonino's foot (not without help from the trapped one, of course), it became clear that his friend could walk only with great difficulty.

In his agitation, Spark arrived at their destination in a matter of moments — only in his thoughts, of course, for it would have been cruel to hurry Tonino along.

"How much longer will we drag ourselves?" he moaned to himself.

"Here we are!" Tonino finally said, pausing for breath. "This is the Tufts and Ringlets Machine, the Yushkas' favorite hangout.

"I don't see any machine," Spark responded, for it was pitch-dark.

The next moment he heard a loud, scratching noise as Tonino lit a branch with a steel rod and brought it to a heavy oak door. It illuminated a note that read, "Clozed for the Nite." Below it there was an assortment of little signs.

The light jumped from one sign to the next, all full of orthographical blunders: "Harecuts"... "Kurling ala Perzhun lam"... "Stileing by Khalo"... "Gnots"... "Poeny-tales an Brayds"...

Normally Tonino liked to make fun of Yushkas' scribbles, but now they didn't seem funny to him.

It was clear that they wouldn't be able to warn them of the approaching danger.

Tale V

The Murmoses

Spark walked with his head lowered, his feet groping for the magnetic path as one thought kept churning in his head: How could he ward off the catastrophe that would surely cause great harm to Stella? Everything now appeared to him in the gloomiest light.

"How could I hope that Narcissus would agree to listen to me? After all, he knows nothing of me and I... What do I know of him?"

He reminisced about the miniature book once again — in particular, a chapter titled "On Murmoses' Clan."

Yet the more he remembered, the more he understood that all that seemed familiar to a Stonemason, as he was, was incompatible with the ways the Valley folk reasoned.

"By the time we are talking about," he read in the Medun's Fibs, "only three of the Murmoses were left in Lemon Drop Valley: Narcissus, his daughter Mura, and Madame Keks.

"These three Murmoses, although similar in some respect, differed in temperament, especially when matters were concerned of purely trifling things... such as tails...

"Narcissus' daughter, Mura, was growing so quickly that she missed that crucial age when daughters were being espoused, and due to that fact she had accepted her tail for what it was and even found it a bit charming...

"As far as Narcissus and Madame Keks were concerned, their affair with their tails was winding up differently. Can you imagine, they felt strangely shy of their very presence!

"Yet if Narcissus had tucked his in a pocket made of softest leather (and thanks to this trick managed to simply erase it from his memory for quite some time), the situation with Madame Keks was rather different.

"Strictly speaking, she lost her tail as far as her youth. And no matter how much she tried to conceal this fact, it occupied the minds of Valley folk who, it might be supposed, hadn't better things to think about.

23

"Some swore that Volchak the General impulsively gnawed off Madame Keks' tail while they were playing a game of croquet. Others insisted that her tail got burned when touched by a torch that the General's brother-in-law habitually swung.

"By the by, it was at this time when a bad reputation began to arise about the Volchaks. They were even called a terrible name that was absolutely banned in the Valley.

"Of course, if you solemnly swear not to spread it around like a common village gossip, you will be allowed to learn that their name is VILMONSTERS.

"In all fairness, one needs to clarify that Narcissus' timidity with respect to his tail was reflected in his eyes.

"An explanation is in order. The nature of the Murmoses' eyes was such that they were situated in a close proximity to each other, thus making their owners somewhat cross-eyed.

"Narcissus' eyes, however, beyond their general cross-eyed nature, were incapable of focusing on any object with confidence. That was because recently he had inexplicably begun to confuse the color of carrots and chinchillas so that orange looked like brown and vice versa. It's true, he was able to see other objects perfectly, although for some reason they appeared to resemble each other very closely..."

Now it may be quite clear to you why Spark felt he understood very little of what he had remembered. Less than little, in fact, which is an optimistic way of saying "absolutely nothing at all."

Yet if Spark was confused now, events would soon develop with such speed that would leave him utterly flummoxed!

The Tufts and Ringlets (T&R) Machine

Lemon Drop Valley was getting ready for the Grand Opening of Aboo-Kaboom. The seashore was literally dammed up with folks, everyone babbling about transformation miracles, donkey roasts, chinchilla balls, and goodness knows what else!

Local society women had been busy creating new outfits. Mura commissioned a chinchilla manteau to be made for the event. Yet as no precious fur could be found in Lemon Drop Valley, she was left with no option but a chinchilla-tinted fox jacket. Beauty couldn't be sacrificed, you know! New hats, silks and laces, beaded clutch bags and other doodads were fetched from the trunks. Houses were painted, silver dinnerware was polished, and a Lemon Drop Valley banner was hung near the monument with a candied lemon torte embroidered on it.

And the beautiful Yushkas literally besieged the Tufts and Ringlets Machine.

"Get orderly, girls!" Madame Keks commanded them, consulting her customer register. "Stella goes after Pigly..."

And Pigly was falling head-first into the T&R Machine where scissor-combs performed their magic dance over her. She was then transported along a moving belt into the shower, the dry-off compartment, and finally into the curling chamber.

And out of the T&R Machine's exit came a long woolen thread.

So that's what the precious Yushka fur was used for! Textile machines noisily rattling nearby were weaving the thinnest signature fabric...

At last the sweet-smelling Pigly jumped out with a new hairstyle called the "Gnot." And the rest of Yushkas surrounded the glamorously transformed Pigly to ooh and ahh, nodding their heads and tugging at her ringlets...

Then the maw of the Tufts and Ringlets Machine opened up again in order to admit the beautiful Stella.

And precisely at that moment the sweet turn of events showed its sour side.

"Think of me as a real chinchilla!" Stella yelped, moving her shoulders. "And should I share the excess of my beautiful fur with anyone, I would sooner do that under the glass cupola of Aboo-Kaboom, and not here!"

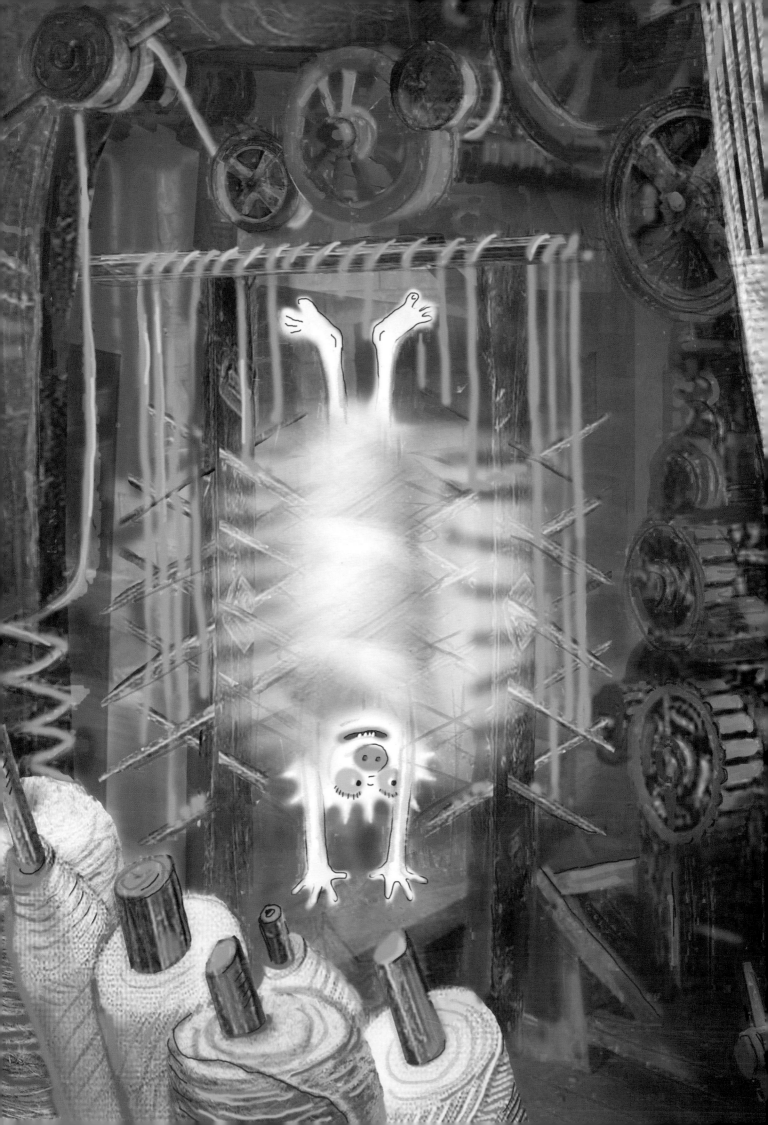

Having said that, Stella flew out of the door, leaving Yushkas perplexed, for the last thing they could expect was this turn of events.

The First Great Event that Shook the Valley

On top of Aboo-Kaboom's glass cube was Narcissus' daughter, Mura the Murmose. She sat with her legs crossed and her luxurious tail spread out for all to see. She twirled a large multicolored umbrella over herself in such a way that one might actually believe she was spinning the solar disk.

Papa Narcissus was proudly posing in a new frock coat and spats.

"Ladies and Gentlemen! Try to imagine the unimaginable!" Madame Keks trumpeted. "Before your very eyes Stella the Yushka will turn into Her Majesty, Queen Chinchilla! And a chinchilla ball will be given in her honor!"

At the sound of an orchestra Stella appeared before the Kaboom.

Gracefully, she freed herself from a blue silk robe and graciously permitted the crowd to admire her fluffy white fur. Then she coquettishly pulled off her blue beret and threw it to the delighted crowd.

Spark's thoughts started to rush higgledy-piggledy.

"What will happen next? How beautiful she is!" he thought. He was still out of breath from their zippy walk.

Due to their late arrival they had to settle for a less-than-ideal spot at the far edge of the crowd. Alas, their late arrival was unavoidable. Tonino suspected that Valley folk who had never seen a Stonemason before might be unfriendly toward Spark, so he came up with the idea to buy a hooded coat for his friend. A sound idea, Spark had agreed, but the purchase took precious minutes they would have needed to arrive on time for the ceremony.

So, the festivity was already in full swing when they showed up.

Now Mura touched the glass basket with her pointer, releasing the colorful balloons.

28

Paint burst from them as they rolled, spraying a rainbow of colors into the air. Screams of delight resounded in the crowd.

"Long live the Chinchilla Queen!"

"Hail the new dynasty! The Chinchillas!"

Beaming with pride, Narcissus took aim with his rifle and fired a few celebratory volleys into the skies.

Yet the joyful outburst stopped just as suddenly as it had started.

The magic had failed.

A solid stream of orange paint started to dribble from the ceiling. Instead of turning into a chinchilla, Stella remained steadfastly a Yushka, only a Yushka freshly painted in fluorescent carrot orange, as if someone had switched on an electric light bulb inside of her.

"Fraud!" Madame Keks screeched, at once forgetting her good manners. "Where is that numbskull, that... that rotten engineer?"

"Drown him like a rat!" Narcissus screeched in turn and then added in a querulous tone, "Er, what's the matter, anyhow?"

Nothing had gone wrong, as far as he could tell. As he was unable to differentiate carrot orange from chinchilla brown, he had been convinced that everything was moving according to plan.

But the spectators told him otherwise, the air now filled with their giggles, whistles and hoots of derision.

Stella hunched her head between her shoulders, trembling as she fought back tears. What a shameful, humiliating disgrace!

Spark's heart palpitated with pity.

"You are splendid, my Princess!" he heard his own voice cry out.

But what was that? Dropping to one knee, Super-Pyzhik suddenly appeared at Stella's side, giving his solemn promise to her:

"I'll be your brave knight!"

Deceptive Step

No, it was unbearable to watch this!

Spark broke away from the crowd and rushed off, seeing nothing ahead of him.

Tonino followed, barely able to keep apace with him.

"Why should he and not I be her brave knight? Why is it with all my careful planning and devotion, others —" Spark muttered, his voice breaking with emotion.

Yet Tonino didn't respond.

"If it were not for him, I would be the first to drop on my knee!"

"You seem to have contemplated the topic of a knee at length," Tonino said unperturbedly. "But now think of the vile Zhabrey who played his dirty trick on Stella."

"Yes, yes, indeed!" Spark said feverishly. "The brave knight will be the one who will track the villain!"

"And how do you imagine this to happen? Do you think the villain will tip off his hat and pronounce you the knight? No, my dear friend, you must track him down and make him harmless. Are you ready?"

"Yes,! And you?" Tonino said with a note of trepidation. "But Zhabrey is not to be trifled with. Before you commit yourself, you must weigh it over very carefully."

"Count me in!" said Spark. "But what exactly am I to weigh over?"

"For example, a step before his dungeon that looks like a rock face... Remember? Well, if you miss that step you would never find it again, would you?"

"Understood. But what if that step is in fact a rock face?"

"That's the most difficult part. As there is no way for two people to step there, you will have to find it on your own!"

"Understood again! But if this is such a serious matter," Spark said, feeling a bit overwhelmed, "perhaps we should wait for a favorable moment..."

"Consider that it had come! Somewhere here must be the entrance to Zhabrey's dungeon!" Tonino whispered. "It's believed that one couldn't spot it even if one's nose were up against it. So, I'll go first and you watch my steps. You will have to repeat them precisely!"

Tonino ran ahead, soon disappearing from sight.

"So, where is the tricky spot?" Spark thought and darted after Tonino.

He was certain that he was repeating Tonino's every step. Yet when he placed his foot on the dangerous step, something collapsed under him and he dropped like a stone.

Spark must have been grateful for being born a stone man, for the sound smack on the back of his head he received when he landed caused him very little injury — that is, if one discounts the fact that he completely forgot everything that happened before.

His memory failed to even keep a thought of Tonino. Yet what really happened to his friend he couldn't have imagined even in his grimmest nightmare!

The Second Great Event that Shook the Valley

The dramatic events surrounding the Aboo-Kaboom didn't come to an end with our friends' departure.

Super-Pyzhik remained frozen in his kneeling position, and the hushed crowd also froze as they awaited the response from the sorrowful and devastated Stella.

Suddenly a piercing scream came from Mura the Murmose from atop the Aboo-Kaboom: "Volchaks!"

And then three things happened at once.

Stella rushed to Super-Pyzhik and clung onto his neck. The Volchak leaped out of the bush and, having snatched Lusha the Yushka, artfully maneuvered towards the woods. Panic set in.

"Save little Lusha!" Madame Keks cried out after Narcissus, who was already jumping into his cabriolet with his old rifle atilt.

Buksha started with a jerk.

"Run! Come on, you old fleabag! Move it! Giddyap! Commence! Go!"

In that way Narcissus had been spurring his tired Buksha who served him many years and at the same time fired his rifle in all directions, but the distance between himself and the Volchak continued to grow until finally Narcissus threw up his hands in resignation.

"He ran away, the kinless mammoth!

We could have captured him with ease!

Should you speed up, why didn't you, damn it!

You lost your spark, you sordid beast!"

Buksha stopped, turned her head and stared at her master. In that way they stood, looking at each other until all of a sudden Buksha spoke:

"You reached your life's apocalypse!

Look at yourself! You've missed the game:

Volchak is loose and, read my lips:
You are the only one to blame!"

To say Narcissus was taken aback would be an understatement.

"Well, I'll be darned... You can talk!" he said, or, rather, wanted to say, for nothing except for red balloons came out of his mouth with letters and runes that rhymed and sang:

"What shall we do to find a fix?
How shall we tame this savage monster —
To keep in check his sharp unguis
And help our confidence to bolster?"

Buksha, the bronco, instantly snapped back the solution:

"You marry off your daughter Mura...
Opt for Volchak as her consort...
She'll find in him a solid mural —
I mean, support (or last resort)
To keep us all out of danger,
Guard our livelihood and manger!"

Narcissus heard Buksha's words in a speechless rapture. He understood only too well that Murmosa Mura did need a strong hand.

"Well, what about him?" Narcissus asked by belching red balloons into the air. "Would he even want to marry her?"

"Don't think so."

"So what's there to do?" a new balloon emerged from Narcissus' mouth.

"We'll have to wheedle him into doing it."

As you can see, Narcissus and Buksha's way of dispatch was in a shambles. Shambolic was the time, and messy were the thoughts of every one in this bash. It had hitherto never happened that the Volchak snatched anyone in full view of all. Frightened Yushkas and Pyzhiks herded together to hear Super-Pyzhik who stepped in front of them:

"In times of hardship and desolation
We need to reckon hard and fast
Where to look for consolation
And whom to place before the mast..."

But as soon as Pyzhiks and Yushkas prepared themselves for reckoning "hard and fast," Narcissus showed up driving his cabriolet.

"Get moving, everyone! Important news!" he bellowed by his now all too familiar way of belching red balloons into the air.

Standing next to Stella, Super-Pyzhik discreetly took her by her delicate paw.

"Ah!" murmured Stella with downcast eyes. "I'm such a mess. I didn't even have time to fix my hair."

But Super-Pyzhik couldn't have cared less since he was head over heels in love with Stella the Yushka!

Narcissus, clad in his new frock coat, hopped off his cabriolet and stepped to the middle of a meadow. Before the bewildered crowd, red balloons flew up that read:

"I've reached my life's apocalypse!

It's time to rein in the warfare

And turn the Valley, fair and square,

Into a heaven: read my lips!

I'll marry off my daughter Mura,

Opt for Volchak as her consort...

He'll bust a gut to be her mural —

I mean, support of any sort!"

And he flung open the doors of his cabriolet, out of which appeared General Volchak, dressed up in a formal general's uniform.

First, the General approached Madame Keks, clicked his heels, reached into his jacket and presented her with little Lusha, who, having spent some time in the dark, was rapidly blinking her eyes.

Then in a ceremonial step he approached his intended and offered her his arm, bent at the elbow.

Mura tried to look away but Narcissus walloped her in the back rather painfully, having thus blessed their match.

The General and Mura paraded to the cabriolet, Madame Keks and Narcissus proudly marching after them. Buksha solemnly circled the meadow as petrified Yushkas and Pyzhiks looked on.

"Everyone is expected at the wedding!" shouted the bronco on Narcissus' behalf.

"I told you that the ball wouldn't be cancelled!" added Madame Keks.

The Protective Medallion

Although all the events of this ill-starred day had been completely erased from Spark's memory (thanks to his nasty fall en route to Zhabrey's habitat, as you will recall), other things remained intact and clear. And he kept wondering: where could Tonino have disappeared to?

Is it any wonder Spark was ready to suspect the worst? But what was the worst?

At the sunset he darted off to the Old Oak Valley hollow to find his friend. But when he arrived, not only could he not find any trace of Tonino, he couldn't find any trace of the Old Oak Valley hollow! Even the old oak tree was impossible to find.

He then rushed off to the promenade and toured four rounds about it. All his endeavors proved to be futile. Tonino wasn't anywhere to be found!

Spark cursed himself for not having asked Tonino his address. There was still one last place to look — the forest. But how could one search in that dangerous place, when all its inhabitants hide from one another?

A thought of Granite Mountain — safe, wide-open Granite Mountain! — came to mind and gave him a pang. How he longed to be there right now!

"What if I also get snared into a trap? Who will help me out then?"

Although this thought pierced him like a needle, he was already moving towards the forest, keeping his ears cocked for tell-tale sounds and taking care not to lose his way.

But the deeper he got into the dark forest, the less hope he had in finding Tonino.

"Don't despair!" he told himself, and he forged ahead.

Soon the forest thinned out and there was more visible moonlight to help him find his way. Suddenly he heard voices, and as he hurried along, a meadow opened up to his full view. The voices were closer now, and Spark rushed to find a place from which he could watch unobserved.

Illuminated by the moonlight, he spied Yushkas and Pyzhiks sitting in a circle. It seemed to Spark that he was witnessing an important meeting.

"We must prepare for an extended battle!" he heard Super-Pyzhik saying.

"And what about the wedding?" all the Yushkas whined in unison.

"The wedding is but a test," Super-Pyzhik replied, "a test verifying whether or not we are scared."

"Well, aren't we?" objected Pigly the Yushka.

"Well, it is not what we think that is important, but what they think. And they will certainly think that we are thinking the same thing as they are! Thus, if we decided to get prepared to an extended battle, and we are going to attend the wedding, that means that it's time to start rehearsing the minuet."

The Yushkas sighed with relief.

"Are we allowed to go and get prepared?" Yushka Pigly asked again. "We have to tie on our festive ribbons, and you know what a time-consuming chore that is!"

The other Yushkas shrieked in agreement. The festive ribbons! How could they have forgotten all about them! And before Super-Pyzhik could say anything in reply, the meadow was nearly deserted. Only Stella remained at his side.

"You are so... smart!" she murmured.

Super-Pyzhik was flattered. Impetuously he took a locket from his neck and handed it to Stella.

"This will save you in the time of danger!" he told her.

Spark screwed up his eyes and, for better security, closed his eyes with his palms.

How he longed to find himself on top of Granite Mountain! How miserable, how lost and alone he felt at Lemon Drop Valley again!

And here is what's amazing. Although Spark's eyes were tightly shut, he didn't miss anything. For example, he saw the image of Super-Pyzhik in his festive attire on his gold medallion, as well as Stella, who stood for a while, pressing the medallion to her chest.

And yet neither Super-Pyzhik, the giver, nor Spark, the accidental seer, could suspect that Stella would remember these words of Super-Pyzhik once again.

The Disrupted Minuet

At the appointed hour the Yushkas and Pyzhiks in all their finery were left standing outside the house of Narcissus, cautiously peeking inside but too shy to enter.

Among them, and no less cautious, was Spark, hopeful that he might find Tonino at the wedding party. Muffled up in his new hooded coat, he entered the home with the others when the doors were flung open. He quickly took a spot in a discreet corner, half-hidden from view by a massive potted geranium.

There were already plenty of guests: three Volchaks — relatives of the General from the neighboring valley — the vampire Shurik, who had been delivered inside a barrelful of seawater, and many more. Narcissus and Madame Keks were sitting near the newlyweds.

As the Yushkas and Pyzhiks made their entrance, the General's relatives jumped up and dashed to the doors in order to count the gifts.

"Way too little!" they wailed after having counted twice all carrot juice bottles and blocks of yarn.

"Boys! Girls!" Madame Keks clamored, grabbing the guests' attention. The Yushkas and Pyzhiks immediately aligned themselves in pairs, preparing for the traditional minuet that habitually opened the wedding ritual.

Then Madame Keks clapped her hands to set the pairs into motion.

Holding his white-gloved paw behind his back, each "boy" started a slow step around his "girl."

Snow-white Yushkas then dropped to curtsey, graciously spreading their upper paws and connecting with the Pyzhiks, then dropping curtseys again to bring their paws to their sides.

They moved away from their partners in order to meet them again and to repeat the very same step many times.

While zealously observing every step of the dance and thinking of no precautions, Spark was eager to mix with the circle of dancers, his arms already feeling a gentle touch...

At this opportune moment we must confess that speaking of snow-white Yushkas and "boys" in white gloves, we have neglected to mention one rather trifling detail that threatened to grow into an event of utmost importance.

The first and most gracious pair was not in white but rather carrot-orange attire. Stella had sensibly refused to wear a white dress, knowing that against its pristine brightness her orange-painted fur would be an eyesore.

As for Super-Pyzhik, he was clad in orange out of solidarity with his chosen one. After all, he was declared her knight from now on!

The minuet had enveloped everyone with its magic spell. Even the General's relatives were mesmerized as they watched the couples move...

But the magic didn't last long.

One of the General's relatives rudely grabbed Yushka Pigly by her tail, and immediately the General smacked his paw.

"The guests are not to be touched!" said the General sternly. "An agreement is an agreement."

"Who's touching?" asked the ill-mannered relative with a smirk, and withdrew his paw, not before patting the Yushka on her cheek.

"I want roast meat," another relative grumbled.

Once again, the General threw a glowering glance in his direction, and the relative quietly withdrew his head into his shoulders.

But the minuet was already disrupted and the spell was broken.

It's hard to predict how the evening would have ended if the last guest — Medun the Senior in his cook's cap — hadn't made his appearance at that moment.

In his paws there was a huge tray with fruit mousse and a heaping bowl of banana and lemon sauce.

Spark recognized Medun the Senior instantly. And his heart sank. He feared his worst fears had come true. "What happened to Tonino?" he thought. "Oh, I am to learn everything from him!"

The Wedding

Who could stand one's ground when faced with a fruit mousse with banana and lemon sauce?

So, it came as no surprise that Medun the Senior's mousse cast a spell on everyone. Having forgotten the disrupted minuet, the hosts and their guests proceeded with the wedding ceremony.

The groom didn't wait long to stick his paw into the mousse tray. And it would be strange if he didn't do it, for he stuck his paw into every pot that required sampling. And since every inch of the serving table had been simply crammed with food, there was no opportunity for boredom.

Only the bride didn't touch the food; she just sat there pouting.

"Oh, this isn't how it's done in other creatures' homes!" she sobbed suddenly.

"Well, what's wrong, my darling?" asked the General anxiously.

"Others have round loaves at their wedding, and what do we have?"

"So it's the loaf you're missing?" the General asked with a grin, revealing two rows of menacing fangs. Loaves I can get, as many as there are small fry around here!

First casting a warning glance at the now-quieted Yushkas and Pyzhiks, he flung open his suitcase and round loaves began to rain all over the table.

True, one of them fell into the barrel of seawater, at which point the vampire Shurik's long green arm became briefly visible as he snatched it.

"Well, did I oblige?" asked the General, grinning at the bride.

Mura capriciously shrugged her shoulders. "And where is the priest? I won't marry without a priest!"

"Is that all you want?" the General chuckled. Once again he stuck his paw into the suitcase... and out he dragged a robed priest by the scruff of his neck. Actually it was a Gorgulia, but she knew her priestly business, all right. And that was the important thing!

"Hello, Shurik!" Gorgulia the priestess nodded to the vampire.

Poking his head briefly out of the barrel, the vampire was just finishing off the last bit of his water-logged loaf.

"Salute to the Servant of the Cult!" he mumbled with his mouth full.

"The Servant of the Cult" cleared her throat, perched a pair of glasses on her nose, and produced a long parchment made of birch bark, rolled up in a tube.

For intolerable minutes she mumbled words under her breath. Finally she shook her head and declared: "I now pronounce you husband and wife!"

All raised their glasses.

The General proposed the toast from which it followed that someone's destiny is being turned to the best. It was unclear however, who were those to benefit from this turn.

"Well spoken!" the relatives all buzzed, while the General stuck his paw into a suitcase and produced a gramophone.

Someone wound up the handle, and the gramophone roared out a rousing march.

Everyone began to dance, including the new Mr. and Mrs., Narcissus and Madame Keks, and Gorgulia the priest with Shurik the vampire.

Meanwhile, Volchak's relatives hustled around the tables, scavenging everything that was left and stuffing it in their maws.

The march was followed by a quadrille. Everyone danced in his and her own style.

After a brief whispered conference with the Pyzhiks, the Yushkas also joined in with the crowd, but as soon as they found themselves near an open door, they made a quick getaway.

Of course, Spark noticed their escape and mentally applauded them, rejoicing that their maneuver had gone unnoticed.

Yet it was premature to be jubilant!

When a tricky dance step threw Mura to the place where Yushkas and Pyzhiks had been only a moment ago, Volchak cut everything short.

"Where're the small fry?" he yelled, and kicked the gramophone with such force that it made one last squeak and became silent forever.

But the small fry were long gone! No evidence of their escape, not even their footprints!

The General gave the musical box a final kick and ran out of the house. His relatives galloped behind him, and the house was now empty, not counting the sobbing bride.

Spark, too, darted outside. For a moment he thought he saw a cook's cap among the branches. Yet as his eyes adjusted to the darkness, he was convinced Medun had disappeared, leaving no trace.

It was as though the earth had swallowed him up.

The Pursuit

As the Volchaks made their way out the door, snow began falling. This might have gone unnoticed on any other winter day in Lemon Drop Valley. But it wasn't any other winter day. In fact, it wasn't even winter.

Imagine, on a warm summer evening, amid the green foliage and fragrant flowerbeds — a snowstorm!

The Volchaks, of course, had no clue that behind this miracle was the Great wizard Lestro, who had conjured it to hide the white-gowned Yushkas under a snow-white cover.

The snow fell in heavy flakes, and within a minute the entire Valley seemed painted white. But that's not all! The snow danced most heavily over the Volchaks, blinding them so that they began bumping into each other like newborn kittens.

"All go to the attic — bring me a pair of binoculars!" ordered the General, and he bolted back inside the house and up the stairs.

Although the attic offered a panoramic view of the Valley, he searched in vain but could see no one in the driving snowstorm.

"They got away, the rogues!" cursed the General.

Then, just when he was about to give up, he spotted a bright orange blob in the distance.

"Here, here, my little lost one! Now you won't get away!"

Without wasting any time, the General took off toward the Valley.

Well, he wasn't wrong about the "lost one." It was Stella, who, because of the freak snowstorm, failed to follow her friend and was about to settle in the snow...

But then she heard the echo that she took to be the voice of Super-Pyzhik. So, she

sniffed the air, trying to figure out from which direction her salvation was coming. Her heart was beating with joyful relief.

But it was the General who now stood right in front of her.

Stella darted to the side. The General maneuvered to block her passage. The Yushka saw the General's mouth widen in a predatory grin. He was so close that she felt his foul, hot breath.

But suddenly his mouth snapped shut. The General yelped in pain, his body sinking to the ground.

Behind him crouched Super-Pyzhik, who had just bitten his tail.

But Stella never learned that, because she left so quickly that she didn't even have time to think about the road that she was running on.

But it was just as well, because there was no road for the Yushka to follow. There was only a crevice of Granite Mountain, which Stella promptly fell into.

Poor Stella! She was falling into a place hardly ever reached by a living creature. This meant that even if she would not be dashed to pieces on the jagged cliffs, she would certainly die from starvation.

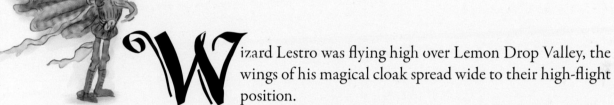

Granite Mountain

Wizard Lestro was flying high over Lemon Drop Valley, the wings of his magical cloak spread wide to their high-flight position.

"What will become of Mash-fatum after my death?" he thought to himself. "My successor will need time to get prepared... perhaps a year or two. Meanwhile, should Mash-fatum fall into the wrong hands, what would become of Lemon Drop Valley folk? Yes, one needs a secure hiding place for Mash-fatum."

As he knew no secure place other than Granite Mountain, towards Granite Mountain he was heading.

He flew with no breaks for resting or eating, fearful that his strength might abandon him half way.

"Will I ever reach its summit?" despaired the wizard and then, suddenly, he saw a plateau submerged in snow. Stone boulders darkened here and there, as if some giant had strewn them around along the vast field of snow.

Yet Lestro barely chanced to take a few steps, when the boulders came to life and slowly approached him, forming a circle.

They moved with heavy steps casting down their heads.

"Are they stonemasons, the eternal inhabitants of Granite Mountain?" wondered the Great wizard.

Yes, they were.

Suddenly, one of them stepped forward and Lestro saw something that nothing but magic could explain. Slowly the boulder lifted its eyelids, and where there should have been eyes, two emeralds shone, emitting green rays of light. And yet they were eyes — or rather, eyes and emeralds at the same time, that belonged to the old King of the stonemasons.

Despite his secret name, Misparko-Para-Sol-Spark-Ling
(which, you might remember, was so long due to his
many legendary exploits), the stonemasons called their
ruler Spark-ley for short, and even immortalized it
in their anthem:

Our rocks have been wizened,
Sharp as the fins!
We have been chiseled
After the Sphinx.

Spared of possessions
Other than, Hey!
The wisdom and might
Of our King, Spark-ley!

"Who are you, and what are you doing here at such an inapproachable height?" asked King Spark-ley in a voice resembling the sound of grinding rocks.

Of course, it didn't occur to him that a great wizard would pay a visit to stonemasons. King Spark-ley grew silent as he awaited the stranger's response, and at last it came:

"I am the wizard Lestro. And I have come to tell you that your letter reached me too late. My magic power is about to expire. However, I have a counter-request for you."

He did not utter another word.

Nor did the King ask for one.

So they stood there for about an hour or two in complete silence.

Behind the stonemasons stood Spark, who kept himself hidden from view. He certainly didn't want the wizard to identify him as a casual visitor to his castle! Now he prayed silently, "Oh, mightiest Lestro, trust the word of our King!"

And Lestro must have heard his prayer.

He flung open his black cloak, took the Mash-fatum out and, after viewing all the stonemasons, said this:

"I humbly ask Your Majesty to keep this magic Mash-fatum until it is claimed by a new wizard..."

"... new wizard..." the Granite Mountain echoed back.

"He will fly to you riding on a luminous comet!" said the wizard.

"... on a luminous comet..." The echo reverberated again.

"On a luminous comet!" intoned the austere stonemasons, echoing the echo.

And now the King did something quite momentous. From his pocket he produced a chisel and now started to chisel out the words of a terrible oath in their Holy Book. As he worked, his emerald eyes threw their magical radiance to every chiseled word.

And while the King was occupied with his solemn business, Lestro acquainted himself with the content of the Holy Book, which consisted of nothing but oaths.

"Conceal and hide," Lestro read. "Be as the rocks, and wish for nothing other than what you already have. The Sphinx taught us how to keep silent, for it is in silence that we maintain secrets…"

"Truly, they know how to be quiet!" thought Lestro, now confident that Mash-fatum truly would be in reliable hands. "I swear on Zeus' name, there are no people more trustworthy than the stonemasons!"

Meanwhile a new oath was hewn on the cliff, and the stonemasons repeated its words all together:

"We, the tribe of the stonemasons, do solemnly swear to keep the secret of the Mash-fatum until the end of the world or until the reappearance of the wizard riding on a luminous comet."

When the ritual was finished, all turned their heads to the Great wizard who whispered his final word to the Mash-fatum, spun around the handle and…

The rocks were set ablaze by the sacred flame that started on its own, warming up the stone bodies of the stonemasons.

The mountain Spirits danced inside the flame petals and it was impossible to take one's eyes off their sacred dance. As the stonemasons stared at the dancing flame, they hummed in delight.

"Now I can die in peace," murmured the wizard by way of a farewell.

The stonemasons lowered their heads following their custom.

Having taken off his Flyer-Boots and his cloak, Lestro waved his hands. And both magical objects vanished into thin air. Then he looked over Lemon Drop Valley with sadness in his eyes and, slowly approaching the edge of the cliff, he stepped forward…

A grinding moan escaped the lips of the stonemasons.

"Now he will be dashed against the rocks!" one cried.

But, no! To their astonished eyes the wizard Lestro fell as a feather, and then began an improbable ascent — higher and higher, gradually turning into a light cloud reminiscent of the frigate *The Silver Fleece*.

Meeting the Yushka

Spark watched as the wizard took his leave.

When there was nothing left to see, he climbed atop the big Coral stone and tossed a piece of tourmaline into the Valley. With a chagrined expression on his face he followed its path to the bottom. It was easy to spot when it landed, as it turned from green to dark lilac in the shining sun.

But what was this?

The tourmaline had landed next to a little orange-colored clod that was lying motionless. Spark looked and looked and couldn't believe his eyes.

"*Rambulla!*" he yelled in the ancient language of the stonemasons.

Of course he hadn't mastered that language yet, but he liked this particular word so much that he pronounced it whenever he wanted to tell something very important. And the news he wanted to deliver was indeed very important. There was no doubt about it; he had recognized Yushka Stella as the orange-colored clod!

So he rushed to the hooting stone located next to the Holy Book and struck it with all his might.

"*Rambulla!*" he shouted again. "*She is dying down below! We must hurry and rescue her!*"

Not a moment had passed before the stonemasons began to crawl out of every mountain crack and crevice.

They felt sorry for the living creature that was dying. They had kind souls. However, Paragraph 11 of the Great stone book of Oaths and Commandments contained one important clause:

"There is no space for Valley folk on the Granite Mountain! Those who are not made out of stone don't know how to keep a secret."

No one could break that clause. No one, that is, but the King of Granite Mountain! And the stonemasons looked at their King, awaiting his wise decision.

But the King was silent, and the stonemasons bowed their heads, feeling compassion for the poor creature that was doomed to die at the bottom of the crevice.

"If you allow her to die..." Spark cried out in desperation, surprising himself with his sudden burst of courage. The code of the stone men didn't permit any challenge to their King, and what Spark was about to say was a direct challenge to their sacred law.

"If you don't allow me to rescue this poor creature, your subjects will never leave the edge of the cliff. Pity will begin to weather them, wearing away on the inside, much like water wears down a stone... Our hands will lose strength... The living cliff will no longer give birth to any stonemasons. Our lineage will disappear and nothing but dead stones will be left of us!"

The King grew pensive.

"You will save the creature from the Valley," said the King at last. "But remember, she cannot ever leave Granite Mountain. All our secrets must die along with her death!"

Oh, how blissful little Spark became! So blissful that he was about to rush down to the bottom of the crevice without remembering to thank his King.

But then he suddenly stopped, realizing that he couldn't rescue Stella! After all, the secret of "The Coveted Path" that he privately knew couldn't be disclosed to others...

So, he stopped as if he were rooted to the ground.

Meanwhile the stonemasons were busy making a steel cable device that would function as a swing. It would bring Spark down the crevice to rescue Stella.

The Prisoner

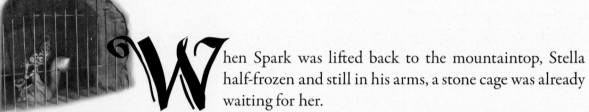

When Spark was lifted back to the mountaintop, Stella half-frozen and still in his arms, a stone cage was already waiting for her.

Granted, this meant bitter imprisonment. But Stella was much too weak to understand that, let alone protest it. In fact, she was barely conscious.

As soon as the prisoner was placed in her cage, the stonemasons gathered around to examine her.

The prisoner didn't seem to be breathing.

"Bring some rock face water from the healing spring!" ordered the King.

And so a ladle of rock face water was delivered and the Yushka sipped it. True, she didn't actually sip it herself. Her little teeth had to be gently unclenched in order to pour the water into her mouth.

It was very quiet as everyone waited for the cure to take effect.

Finally Stella opened her eyes.

"It tastes lousy!" she croaked in a weak voice and looked around. "Where am I?"

"On top of the mountain!" said the stonemasons in unison.

"And who are you?"

"We are the stonemasons," they replied.

"What are you doing here?"

"We live here."

"And why am I here?"

"You are our prisoner."

"For how long?" she asked, and when no answer was forthcoming, she added in a frightened tone, *"For good?"*

As the stonemason nodded their heads, Stella started to weep. "Farewell, my dear girlfriends! Farewell, Super-Pyzhik, my brave knight!" she cried bitterly, touching the medallion that hung around her neck.

"I want food!" she demanded, having wept to her heart's content, "I want carrot juice!"

The stonemasons fell deep into thought. Having spent their entire lives on Granite Mountain, they had no clue what a "carrot" was!

So, they thought very hard, but couldn't come up with anything.

"Oh, I remember!" King Spark-ley exclaimed. "A carrot is a kind of red icicle that the Valley folk stick into the ground."

The stonemasons brightened up. They too knew what an icicle was! Every winter icicles appeared on Granite Mountain in bundles, and the stonemasons loved to suck on them! However, they could hardly imagine why the Valley folk would color them red and stick them into the ground. It seemed rather frivolous.

Anyhow, they all began to chisel icicle "carrots" out of the mountain crystal in order to make juice out of them. In all fairness, they did try very hard. After all, they were the hardest working folk on earth! But all their work was in vain. They didn't know what Stella knew — that one couldn't possibly eat a carrot made out of icicles.

But it was precisely these iridescent icicles that were being carried with great ceremony inside stone platters on top of the heads of three stonemasons.

They solemnly placed the platters in front of Stella, anticipating her delight.

"You want me to die of starvation? You might as well bury me under the ice right now!" Stella hollered looking dismally at the icicles that were placed on stone plates.

Poor Stella! She could no longer think of anything but her death! So she spent her nights curled up in a ball and shivering.

And she would have certainly died, hadn't she already acquired a secret admirer — which was, of course, none other than little Spark.

Spark thought about her when he went to bed, all through the night, in the morning, during the day and then all over again in the evening. And it was indeed Spark who found a path to her salvation.

By chance Spark happened to notice the little scraggly bits of yellowish roots and herbs that poked out of the snow-covered mountain clefts. And secretly he began to pick them so that at night, illuminated by the dancing Sacred Flame, he could provide the prisoner with a simple supper.

And to insure that her supper wasn't too bland, he mixed it up with a spoonful of maple syrup that he used to dress up his own solitary tea parties. These nocturnal hours, when the stonemasons were sleeping soundly after a day of hard labor, were a time of perfect bliss for Spark!

Soon enough Stella's fur regained its glitter, and one night
Spark dreamed that he was playfully pulling her fluffy tail.
Of course, it was only in his dreams that he could
be so bold. But one night, fully awake, he was
overpowered by his desires.
"Mind if I pet you?" he asked to his
great embarrassment.
"Well, of course, I do!" she
replied casually, having
dangled her tail right in
front of his nose.

"Oh, why didn't you just let me die?"

"Are you really so unhappy with us?" Spark asked, unable to take his eyes off her dangling tail.

"How could I be happy? Please! I'm in a cage. I'm used to running, looking around, dancing…" she replied.

Spark quickly reached out and touched Stella's tail.

"Ouch!" exclaimed the Yushka. "You pinched my fluffy tail, you clumsy oaf!"

She turned around, glanced at the medallion that hung around her neck, moved her fluffy tail to the other side of the cage and began to sing a sad song

It's deathlike and cold
In this cage with no leaves
No branches to hold
A prison this is.

And as she sang, little Spark's heart was breaking apart with pity.

"Do you want me to show you our Sacred Flame?" he blurted out.

"Sure, I'd like to!"

"You won't run away? Will you?"

"Where would I run? There's nothing but rocks around here!"

"Still, promise that you'll immediately return to the cage."

"I swear!" exclaimed the Yushka.

The fire was blinding. It gave off such heat that Stella warmed up right away. She turned toward it, first one side then the other, reaching towards it with her slender, frozen paws. All the while the mountain spirits tirelessly danced in the flame petals.

"It's time," Spark said hesitantly. "We must return."

"In a moment!" Stella replied while wandering around the sacred flame with softened eyes.

And then she spotted the Mash-fatum that was gleaming in the flickering fire.

"Wow, what's that?" she exclaimed.

"Quiet! It's a secret!"

"Are there such secrets in the world?"

"What do you mean by 'such secrets'?"

"I mean secrets that are kept even from those there's no reason to keep them from," said the clever prisoner. "Am I not to remain here forever?"

Spark pondered. The Yushka was right. If she never returned to the Valley, then there was absolutely no reason to keep secrets from her, was there?

"Tell me your secret," continued the Yushka, "and I will let you pet my fluffy tail."

And she placed her little tail right next to Spark's hand.

"The secret of the stonemasons," he said while gawking at her glamorous tail, "is this magic Mash-fatum left to us by the Great wizard Lestro."

"And how do you know that it still works? If you keep a mechanism outside, it will surely break."

"This is a magic mechanism, though."

"Doesn't matter," she insisted. "As long as it's a mechanism, it can break. But we can check that out to make sure if you want."

"How?"

"Request something from it."

"I don't need anything,"

"Then ask it your name. It should know it. Shouldn't it?"

"Of course it does!"

"Oh, please! Prove it!"

"I will!"

"You can't! You won't be able to!" teased Stella with a toss of her curls.

"Fine, look."

And thus vexed, Spark turned the magic handle of the Mash-fatum and blew into its tube. Then, once the machine got into gear and began to make a tapping and whistling noise, he heard the voice of the Yushka that ordered:

"Down, to the Valley!"

And down she winged her way.

What will happen to our characters next, you will learn in the third book. Also, the author promises you that as soon as the book you hold in your hands has been read eighteen times, the new book will be waiting for you on the bedside table.

Contents

SPARK THE STONE MAN
Second Book of the First Series

PUBLICATION DATE: AUGUST 2011

PRINTED IN CHINA.
CPSIA Section 103 (a) Compliance:
www.beaconstar.com/consumer
ID: K0116431
Tracking No.: K0312131-7025

TECHNICAL DATA:
Trim pages: 8.5" x 11" Upright, 72 pp + case
Text: (4x4) color on 115 gsm matt paper
Ends: plain on 120 gsm wood free
Case: (4x4) color + film matt lamination on 128 gsm glossy over 2,5 mm board
Case bound: sewn in 16 pp, with separate glue ends, fully cased.

PRICE: $ U.S. 21

ISBN: 978-0-9828487-3-9
LCCN: 2010911130.

Pekasus
Factory of Animated Dreams

tel.: 1 (650) 681-9703 (in the U.S.), + 49 7632 823011 (in Germany),
+ 7 (499) 781-46-08 (in Moscow)
e-mail: Pekasus2011@gmail.com
www.an−animation.com